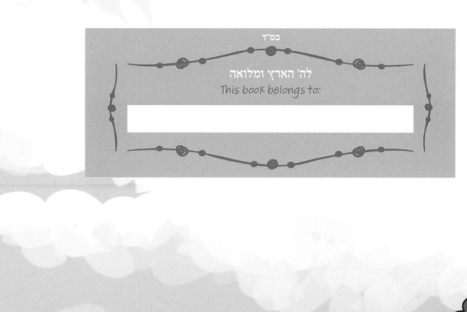

בס"ד

לה' הארץ ומלואה

This book belongs to:

*Dedicated with love and gratitude
to my parents;
my mother-in-law;
my wife, Chanie;
and all my children,
who inspire and encourage me
to pursue my dreams.*

— M.M.M.

THE PRINCE WHO FORGOT

The Baal Shem Tov's Mashal

By Rabbi Mendel Moscowitz

Illustrated by Rodrigo Paulo

DISTRIBUTED BY FELDHEIM

ISBN: 978-965-7041-33-8

Cover Design: Adeeba Sial
Graphic Design: JewishSelfPublishing
Art Coordinator: Rivka Greenberg

The author can be contacted at TripleMPublications@gmail.com.

Printed in China

Distributed by:
FELDHEIM PUBLISHERS
POB 43163, Jerusalem, Israel
208 Airport Executive Park
Nanuet, New York 10943

Distributed in Europe by:
Lehmanns
+44-0-191-430-0333
info@lehmanns.co.uk
www.lehmanns.co.uk

Distributed in Australia by:
Golds World of Judaica
+613 9527 8775
info@golds.com.au
www.golds.com.au

Words in red = important details of the *mashal*
Words in blue = important details of the *nimshal*

The holy Baal Shem Tov asked:

Why do we blow the shofar on Rosh Hashanah?

And he answered with a *mashal*...

THE MASHAL

Once there was a king whose name was King Reginald.
King Reginald ruled over a very large country with many citizens.

The king was a magnificent leader!
He cared for all his people,
and his people loved and respected him.

King Reginald had only one son.

His name was Julius.

Julius was the royal prince.

Julius was quite a genius!

The king loved him
with all his heart.

King Reginald hoped that one day his
beloved son Julius
would become the next king.

But a king needs more than
just a good brain.

He has to be courageous,
and he has to keep his people safe and secure.

He has to be kind and caring and set a
good example for his people.

He has to collect taxes so there will be money
to build roads, bridges, hospitals and schools.

He has to be on friendly terms
with the leaders of other countries.

He has to know how to give marvelous speeches
that will inspire the people.

King Reginald wanted his son to learn all of these skills, and more.

"Where would he learn them?" thought the king.

Then an idea popped into his head.

"I will send off my son to a **faraway land**, where he will meet new people, learn new languages and figure out how to live on his own."

"Perhaps he will enroll in an excellent school where he will learn history, business management and leadership skills, and other important things that he cannot learn in the palace," thought the king.

King Reginald shared his idea with Julius.

"This trip will help you succeed in life," the king said.

The prince had never left home before and was a bit nervous.

But he was also very excited. This was going to be the adventure of a lifetime!
Julius counted the days until his departure.

The big day arrived.

Everyone crowded around the royal coach to wish the prince a safe trip.

King Reginald supplied Julius with everything he would need
for the long journey ahead.

He supplied him with **ministers and assistants**
who would help him succeed.

He supplied him with bags of gold and silver
to help with his expenses.

He supplied him with fancy princely clothes
so he would make a good impression on others.

"Don't forget. You are on a **mission**, so be sure to fulfill it!"
said King Reginald.

"Don't forget. You are very smart, so learn well!"

What happened when Julius arrived in the faraway land?

He forgot the purpose of his trip!

He forgot to sign up for school,
where he would learn important things.

He became friends with lazy and dishonest people.

He wasted all of the
gold and silver
on food and fun.

He didn't take care of his fancy clothes,
and they became torn and tattered.

30

The ministers were upset that Julius didn't take his mission seriously, so they decided to leave him.

After a while, the prince forgot the language
that was spoken in the palace. And when
his money completely ran out,
he became a beggar.

One day, Julius was sitting on the sidewalk, collecting coins in his tin can from people who felt sorry for him.

Suddenly, he heard the sound of trumpets. He looked up and saw the townspeople **cleaning the streets** and decorating the light poles with roses and ribbons!

33

"What's going on?" the beggar-prince asked.

"Didn't you hear the news?" the townspeople replied.

"King Reginald is coming to Calabodia! We are preparing to greet the king!"

"King Reginald? Why, that's my father!" Julius exclaimed.

"You? A prince? You can't be serious! Why, you're just a foolish beggar!" the townspeople said, laughing.

"I've just GOT to see my father, no matter what!" Julius thought.

"Say what you want, but I AM the prince, and I AM going to greet the king!" Julius said with determination.

"You can't greet the king!" the townspeople exclaimed. "Just look at yourself! Your clothes are filthy and ripped, and you probably haven't taken a bath in weeks!"

"Maybe they have a point," Julius thought sadly.
"The king's guards would never allow me to approach the king
the way I look and act."

"Well then, if they don't let me meet the king,
I'll just have to speak to him from way back here!" exclaimed Julius.

"You must be kidding!" they said.
"You don't even speak the language of the king!"

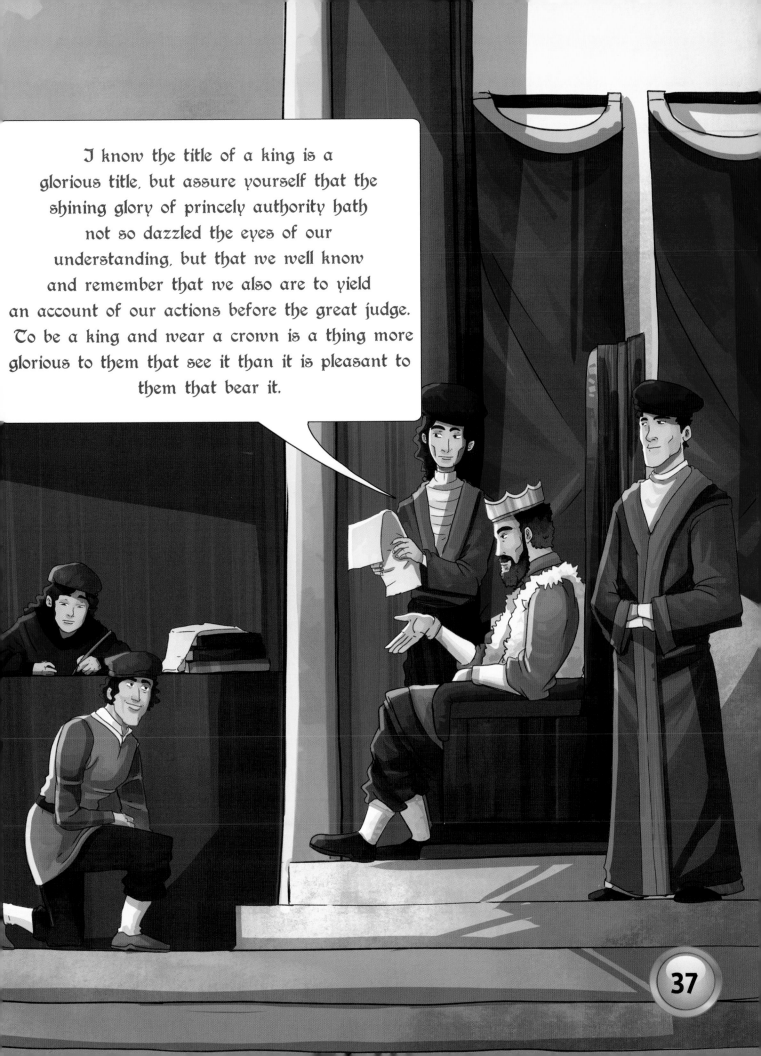

I know the title of a king is a glorious title, but assure yourself that the shining glory of princely authority hath not so dazzled the eyes of our understanding, but that we well know and remember that we also are to yield an account of our actions before the great judge. To be a king and wear a crown is a thing more glorious to them that see it than it is pleasant to them that bear it.

Julius began to sob uncontrollably.

*"These people are right. Just look at me!
I've become a lowly beggar!"*

The beggar-prince turned around and
plopped himself back down on the
sidewalk next to his old tin can.

The day everyone was waiting for finally arrived. Crowds of men, women and children waving flags lined the streets as the royal carriage made its way along the main street of the town.

Julius pushed his way through the crowd,
although it wasn't easy.

"Hey, beggar, you don't belong here!"
some people yelled.

Weeping bitterly, Julius said to himself:
"My looks have changed.
My actions have changed.
My clothes have changed.
Even my language has changed!"

But one thing had not changed: the sound of his voice.

"Oyyy!" the young prince cried out.

Julius's **simple cry** attracted the king's attention.

"That's my son's voice! Julius! It's you!" the king exclaimed. "Thank G-d, you're alive!"

King Reginald gave his son, the prince, a warm hug.

The king brought Julius back to the **palace** in the royal carriage. The prince decided that from then on, he would always obey his father's wishes.

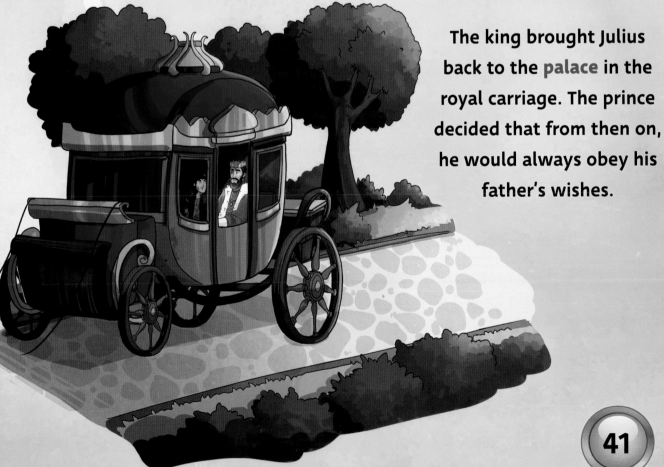

THE NIMSHAL

Hashem

The **king** is Hashem.

The royal **prince** is the *neshamah*,
the Jewish soul.

The **faraway land** **is** this world.

The *neshamah* is sent here in order to learn how to do important things,
like studying Torah, doing mitzvos and davening,
which can't be done in *Shamayim*.

The fancy **princely clothes** are thoughts, words and actions that are appropriate for every Jewish girl and boy.

The **mission** is to make this world a place where Hashem feels comfortable
and to let everyone know that Hashem runs the world
and cares for all His creations.

The ministers and assistants are the **talents**
that help the *neshamah* succeed in its mission.

The bags of gold and silver hint to our love and fear of Hashem.

Unfortunately, a *neshamah* that comes down into the body of a Jewish boy or girl occasionally gets distracted by fun things and forgets what it was sent here to do.

The *neshamah* forgets to use the talents that Hashem gave it.
Without constant practice, those talents begin to get rusty and dusty.

Instead of *loving* Hashem and *fearing* Hashem,
it *loves* playing games and *fears* losing friends
if it tries too hard in school.

Then, one day, the *neshamah* notices people "cleaning the streets." It is the month of Elul, just a few weeks before Rosh Hashanah, and they are preparing to greet Hashem, our Holy King.

The *neshamah*'s friends ask,
"Why aren't *you* getting ready for Rosh Hashanah like *we* are?"

The *neshamah* recalls that it is holy and pure.

"I can't return to Hashem!" the *neshamah* says.
"My thoughts, words and actions are all focused on nonsense!
I even forgot the language of the king—the words of Torah and *tefillah*!"

The *neshamah*'s deepest wish is to reconnect with Hashem. Its only choice is to call out to Hashem, the King, with a simple cry—the cry of the shofar!

"Oy, Hashem, please forgive me for forgetting my mission. But I am Your beloved child. From now on, I promise to act much better, and then..."

...I am certain that You will bring me back to the palace—
Mashiach will take us back to Yerushalayim, this year!"

And that, dear children,
is the Baal Shem Tov's *mashal* for the shofar!

Baal Shem Tov — honorific title for Rabbi Yisrael ben Eliezer (1698–1760), also known as the Besht, who was a great Torah leader from Poland (Ukraine) and the founder of Chassidic Judaism.

davening — praying

Elul — the month of repentence that precedes Rosh Hashanah

Hashem — G-d

mitzvos — good deeds; commandments

Mashiach — Messiah

mashal — parable

neshamah — Jewish soul

nimshal — explanation of a parable

Rosh Hashanah — the Jewish New Year

shofar — a ram's horn, which is sounded on Rosh Hashanah

Shamayim — Heaven

tefillah — prayer

Torah — the commandments and wisdom received from G-d

Yerushalayim — Jerusalem

◆ NOTES ◆

Pages 6–41

Our version of the Baal Shem Tov's *mashal* has been rewritten in a way that children can relate to. It is predicated on the version of the story recorded in the Hebrew book *Elul V'Tishrei* by Toby Hendel and published by Rabbi Y. Y. Kaminetsky.

The following is an abridged, free translation of the original *mashal* as it appears in the *sefer Toras Shmuel* (5637, vol. 2, "V'Kocho," pp. 565–566):

A parable (*mashal*) from Rabbi Yisrael Baal Shem Tov:

Once there was a king who had an only son, the apple of his eye. The son was well-learned and his father loved him very much. One day, the king and the prince decided that it would be educational for the prince to travel to faraway lands to master different fields of knowledge and to experience various cultures.

The king provided the prince with an entourage of ministers and servants as well as a generous supply of money for this expedition, all so that he advance in his knowledge and wisdom beyond his ability to do so at home, in the king's court.

Far from home, the son squandered all the money on the luxuries he was accustomed to at home, plus travel expenses and other excesses that he indulged in during the course of his travels. Eventually, he was left completely destitute and had arrived at a place so far away from home that no one there had ever heard of his father. In addition, no one believed that he was a prince.

Having run out of food and any means to earn a livelihood, the prince decided it was time to return home. But he had been away so long that he had forgotten his native tongue. So when he ultimately made his way back to the capital city of his kingdom, he was unable to explain to anyone who he was and where he needed to go. When he tried to gesture to them that he was the prince, no one believed him. He was ridiculed, beaten and badly bruised.

Finally, when he was near enough to the palace that the king could hear him, in utter despair he began to cry out in a loud voice. The king, who recognized his son's voice, went out and brought him into the palace while showering him with hugs and kisses.

The meaning of the parable (the *nimshal*): The king is Hashem. The prince refers to the souls of the Jewish people, who are called "children of Hashem" (*Devarim* 14:1). The King of all kings sends a soul on a long journey down to this world into a physical body in order to fulfill the Torah and mitzvos. After the soul accomplishes its mission, it can reach greater heights than it could have achieved prior to its descent into this mundane world.

But by indulging in the delights of this world, oftentimes the soul becomes increasingly estranged from its native milieu. It is gradually drawn into an environment that does not recognize G-dliness and is not concerned with it, and it eventually forgets the language of holiness and purity.

At some point, the *neshamah* remembers who it is and cries out to Hashem. This is the wordless blast of the shofar, which utters the innermost voice of the soul in its regret for its past deeds, its longing for its Divine home, and its desire to rededicate itself to its Father. When Hashem hears this cry, it arouses His mercy, and He forgives the *neshamah*, restoring it to its former intimacy with Him.

Pg. 45
The "prince" is a reference to the souls of the Jewish people, who are called the "children of Hashem" (*Devarim* 14:1).

Pg. 48
All human activity is expressed in one of the following three modes: thought, speech or deed. These faculties are known as the "clothing" of the *neshamah*. Each day we clothe ourselves in Divine garments by thinking, speaking and acting in accordance with Hashem's will. (See *Likutei Amarim*, ch. 4.)

The *gemara* (*Bava Basra* 10a) teaches that *tzedakah* is so special that it hastens the redemption.

Pg. 51
The Hebrew word for "silver" is *kesef*, which also means "yearning" and "love" (see *Tehillim* 84:3 and *Zohar* 2:148a). "Gold" symbolizes the fear of being judged (*Zohar* ibid).